POEMS BY CHILDREN

Poems by Children
1950—1961

Chosen by Michael Baldwin

Routledge & Kegan Paul
London

Published 1962
by Routledge & Kegan Paul Ltd
Broadway House, 68–74 Carter Lane
London, E.C.4

Printed in Great Britain
by Cox and Wyman Ltd
London, Reading and
Fakenham

For
PAT BARTLETT

The decorations are by
MICHAEL FOREMAN

Contents

CONTENTS

THE PRINCE'S STEED

THE FACE OF THINGS

CONTENTS

PISTONS

Acknowledgements

I SHOULD LIKE TO THANK first of all the authors who have given me permission to print their work in the following pages, the two thousand teachers and parents who so generously answered an appeal in the press by sending me nearly five thousand poems, and the many others who wrote offering advice and encouragement and expressing their interest.

Special thanks are owing to *Daily Mirror Newspapers* for permission to make use of the top thousand entries for each of three years of their Children's Literary Competition, and for allowing me to quote in the introduction one of the poems printed in their book *Children As Writers;* eighteen of the poems included here are unpublished entries from that competition.

I should also like to thank the many schools who sent me copies of their magazines and anthologies, the editors who made available their back numbers and files, and those who have been generous enough to answer my queries about their contributors; over half of the poems included come from these sources, so it would be an impossibly long list to mention each of the copyright holders by name. Nor is there any way of acknowledging the many schools which are producing and publishing excellent work, but examples of which I have not been able to include.

The following people have most generously allowed me to

quote from their own work on the subject: Mr. David
Shavreen, Mr. W. Eyre, from their theses; and Miss P. E.
Bartlett, Mr. L. G. Kennion and Mr. G. P. White, from
their extensive collections of children's poetry. Mention
should also be made of the unusually high standard of
creative work, of mercifully quite different kinds, submitted
by Hornchurch Grammar School, The Skinner's Company
School for Girls, Stamford Hill, The High School for Girls,
Sutton Coldfield, and Queen Elizabeth School, Kirkby
Lonsdale. Their very full collections did much to stimulate
judgement and establish standards.

Introduction

CHILD ART beckons the plunderer. We make our brief
sorties and return with our fistful of trophies. 'Look what
we have found!' our collections, our competitions, our
books and our articles seem to say. 'Only *we* were capable of
finding it, and only now are you capable of looking. Please
thank us.' Then we grow busy with dogma.

Most of the material in this book has been found for me
by other people, and my task has been the hesitant sifting.
The process is humbling.

Children's Poetry is often second-hand. Not only does its
being quite frequently stem from the insistence of parents
and teachers, but it relies upon them for its transmission as
well. And it is less independent of its means and its circumstances than is adult art; it depends enormously upon our
sense of its context and we have to judge it with standards
that are not always our own. We rarely find, for example,
any evidence of tension between content and style, though
we find content to admire and style to admire and both
very often in harmony: the strife and the triumph of adult
art are absent, even in the frequent works that take strife
or triumph as their subjects. This does not mean that the
eight-year-old or the twelve-year-old is incapable of speaking
with the true voice of feeling. On the contrary. But it does
mean that it is virtually impossible for an adult, especially
one who does not know the child, to be certain what the

true voice of feeling is in a given circumstance. And there are hardly any more objective criteria. *Truth*, we might say, for ourselves. But here we must ask *True to what?* And the answer is: we don't know.

In the absence of any more convincing formula I have chosen the poems I like. This does not mean that I like them in the same way as I enjoy a sonnet of Shakespeare or a lyric by Wordsworth or Auden. Even if it were feasible to measure one poem in terms of another I should still refuse to make the claims, embryonic or actual, that some people make on behalf of children as writers. It would be an embarrassment to my authors and an insult to their intention. If I say that I have chosen the poems that have appealed to me as a writer and a teacher, if I can be as subjective as that (and I know that to be more objective would be to be false to my subject), then perhaps we can do away with any more talk about absolute and relative.

Because I *can* say what poems appeal to me as a writer and a teacher. They are the poems which bring with them the shock of recognition, or, in the absence of that shock (because I cannot always or even often answer *True to what?*) the poems which convince me that the shock should be there and educate me a little way towards it. None of them may be a great poem—the word is irrelevant—but they are all of them good poems, and they have been a part of my growth these last months no less than have the works of the mature poets I have been able to come to freshly during the same period—more freshly, sometimes, because of these.

It is for their own sake, therefore, that I commend them: because I think they matter, not because I think they are documents of educational or psychological interest. This is not an educational book, in the sense that Marjorie Hourd's *Coming Into Their Own* or my *Poetry Without Tears* are educational books. It is not a book about how or why children write poetry at all; it is a book about what poetry they write. In fact, it is not even really about that, because children and child-poets can write bad poetry just as easily as adults and adult-poets, and I do not think we have included any bad poetry, even though it might have been revealing.

*   *   *

We do not always have to search our minds anxiously for standards when judging children's poetry. In this poem by Cleo Geary from the *Daily Mirror* book *Children As Writers*, the author is able to present a very personal anguish in a manner which conforms to our highest notions of truth and freshness, even though she is only eight.

> I wouldn't make friends with me
> I don't like the sound of my voice
> And don't say voices don't count
> Because they do
> My voice lets me down
> It sounds like a boy's
> I don't want a voice that is squeaky and high
> Or a voice that is hoarse and low
> An ordinary voice
> So that I could be
> An ordinary person
> Do you see

But in other poems by this author the style is more mannered even though the talent is equally evident, and it would be impossible to decide whether this is the voice of stylistic innocence or the simplicity which lies beyond sophistication. Like much of the best poetry by children it satisfies our taste much more readily than it allays our curiosity about the processes which produced it.

The above poem has the sort of 'voice' to which many

people in education today are most attracted, but one of the dangers is that those of us who tend to think of ourselves as enlightened often listen for this voice to the exclusion of others. Not only is the idea of being true to experience a misleadingly adult concept (for many children the poem itself *is* the experience) but even where it is applicable we have to realise that children can be true in a different way and to a wider range of feeling than we can. It is easier, for example, for them to be true to the artificial, the phantasmagoric, and the dream, and to come freshly to ideas that an adult would conceive only as a result of deliberate intention.

> The Prince's steed awaits him
> On the cobbly path,
> Legs straight, neck arched,
> Standing under the marble arch.
>
> His mane and tail like silver,
> Against his golden hide,
> Magnificent with his head held high,
> Waiting for a ride.
>
> His hoofs are like glass knives,
> His sparkling wicked eyes
> Glittering like diamonds,
> As they ride across the skies.
>
> As he gallops across the clouds
> He sends a high-pitched neigh
> Cantering amongst the brilliant stars.
> He'll be back next day.

This is no less true than the previous example, and its unity is of a very wonderful order. But surely there are other voices here, or echoes of other voices, heard by the poet and blended by him subconsciously into the single excitement of this poem?

And the child's ability to communicate such excitement *to us* is largely accidental. We speak of liberating expression, and both of these poems would, I take it, be fine examples of liberated expression; but are we sure we really know what we are talking about? For the young child one word is as fresh as another. It is only to us that a phrase can be fresh or stale. One child can write 'my beautiful-eyed bunny' with as much wonder as another who writes 'my bun-eyed bunny' or 'my braille-eyed bunny'; and to another child, reading this example of what is to us the debased *lingua franca* of childhood, 'beautiful-eyed bunny' will convey that wonder, and a picture of a rabbit with eyes, haunted and staring eyes, and that rabbit will dwell in mythology and fable and all of the landscapes of imagination and memory. 'My bun-eyed bunny' will not dwell there, even for its author, because it is definite, and you can only be true to a little at the time— that is his trouble with what adults call images. 'My braille-eyed bunny' will not live anywhere, because he was a lie, made out of words as a result of a certain sort of teaching; but, dead as he is, he cannot be discarded; his author's excitement can live in the texture of the words even though they are, for him, without meaning.

When we talk about young children's writing we are dealing with a world in which 'bunny' is enough. Very often 'bunny' is a whole poem. And this fact must colour all of our notions of 'truth' and of 'liberated expression'. Truth, for the child, is often a lie which he has learned from our image of what we think he should be. The 'liberated' imagination often inhabits a sophistication which, as it grows, will strangle it to death.

* * *

We have seen, in the poem about the horse, how a child is quite capable of producing poetic reality from an area of experience which for us would be entirely literary; and we can perhaps concede that the young poet is the inheritor of an imaginative tradition, a sort of interior landscape, which we are no longer aware of: the echoes which bothered us just a little were archetypal rather than literary, we might argue, and we were dealing with instinctive rather than imitated symbols. Unfortunately this position becomes difficult to maintain in the face of the vast body of literature written by adults for children with the intention of perpetuating this tradition, even if we *can* say that the poem is fresh and organic.

If at this primary level of the imaginative process we are unable to be certain about what is original and true, how can we necessarily condemn poems which are manifestly derivative at the secondary, or stylistic, level? Especially if these poems, as is often the case with the derivative work of young teenagers, have something interesting and personal to say? We may argue that freshness of idiom is more important than originality of content, and that is all we really can say when we defend the primitive; but once more this is an adult judgment, and a shaky one; and reduced to these terms our values seem rather bald. We think we know a great deal about the sort of children's poetry we don't like, because we can detect its influences, and for a child to be stylistically influenced is a major educational sin. But I suspect we don't know nearly enough about the sort of creative near-ecstasy in which a young adolescent can parody and even plagiarise. There is a time in most of our lives when we can hang half the universe on a phrase by Shelley; and what we are trying to tell the world is not the phrase but that part of creation which dangles in its drop of ink.

Therefore I have included some poems which are frankly

literary. Others of them are imitative or show signs of their authors' archiac taste in poetry. The rightness for them of the poetry they read may well result in and be the only cause of the rightness of their poetry for us. So I have thought it proper to accept the work of the child who has read the wrong poetry, but who has something burningly important to tell us.

I have also included poems which are derivative. This may still shock the educators, but I doubt whether it will alarm the literary critic. Every anthology contains lots of derivative poems—obviously derivative, that is: if we were to eliminate the secretly derivative we should have no literature left. I see no reason to judge talented children by harsher standards than we would apply to celebrated and successful adults.

What can we think of a poem like this for example:

Sharks and Swordfish dancing reels,
And monkeys biting fleas,
Pink and green and purple pigs
A-swinging in the trees.

Armadilloes chewing steaks,
And tigers grinding corn,
Guinea-pigs with tails so long
A-beating on the lawn.

Dogs with multi-coloured tails,
Crabs with little nippers.
Blue-nosed whales in uniform
A-wearing purple slippers.

It is a clever poem, of course. And it is literary. Is that a good enough reason for leaving it out?

What of the child who is a humourist? Laughter is rarely the product of the true voice of feeling:

7

My Daddy has a tie.
Can you tell me why?
To put around his neck, of course,
Just like a halter round a horse.

Yet in this poem, which is sophisticated in the extreme, we come very near to the mystery of what is most endearingly childlike. Beside this clever poem a terribly funny one can appear merely clever:

Sandy the pussy has got a sore head
Sandy the pussy has gone to bed,
Sandy the pussy has told me why—
He fell in the washing-machine
And was spun-dry.

It is bad child-writing, of course, but it is good something and it was written by a child. It is hard to deplore it. What *is* good child writing? Very often the excitement of a poem by a child can be traced to a single word, and it is the instinct for this word which has translated it into the region of experience and success:

There was a little bird
What goes twinkling in the trees;
And every time you look at him
He twinkles back at you.
And that is the end of the story.

This poem is delightfully unmannered, and therefore of the type that most experts would praise But I am worried again about our automatic preference for this to a more obviously literary poem. Almost every childish beast has a tail that twinkles. For many children it is a cliché: it is one of the first descriptive words put into their mouths by story-telling adults.

Rare indeed is the statement of wonder that is entirely syntactic, and therefore above suspicion:

> The wee bird
> Creeping up the tree
> Never even heard
> Or saw me.

And rarer still when, as in this case, its author is only seven. Surely the conclusion is that it is impossible to expect too much of children, especially too much originality, the quality which they are generally supposed to display in abundance; we must modify our dogmas a little.

If I have argued over long against what would normally have been my own case it is because a carefully considered scrutiny of the material sent in for this anthology has inclined me that way. It would be pleasant to think that children were always capable of freshness: quite certainly in the present educational environment they are not. In the meantime, as our search for it takes us along the path of what we fancy is liberation and enlightenment, we must be sure that we are not merely choosing an alternative formula of staleness and deceit.

* * *

One of the problems which people have been anxious to face for me is at what age does child-poetry become adult-poetry. Or when, as someone cynically said, does its voice break and it become no poetry at all?

The age which has been most consistently offered has been fourteen. 'You will get nothing after *that*,' I have been told. Or I have been persuaded that, even if I do, it will be outside the scope of an anthology of children's writing.

If it is of a certain sensibility we are speaking, the *innocent* sensibility (and we have seen how bogus or accidental *that* can be) then I agree. It dies much earlier than this. But I must confess I am rather curious to see what it will grow to, given the right circumstances of character and education. Surely we should be rather suspicious of any gospel which contented itself with the miracles?

Then, of course, some children never write in this tradition at all. We have already had to consider examples of an extraordinary sophistication—that *other* tradition. And that grows, or it can grow. The child who is verbally adroit at eight, as distinct from charmingly maladroit, is likely to be so still at eighteen or eighty. Since I received poetry of this modish, imitative, clever (but rarely clever-clever) sort, and sometimes sparklingly funny poems as well, from a variety of age-groups, the problem of where to draw the line still remained; and I came to resent more and more the assumption that it draws itself.

What I said in the end was this: although not everyone who regards himself as a poet is a poet, I think it can be safely assumed that anyone who considers himself a child is a child. Therefore I would accept as eligible any poetry submitted to me by any author who knew clearly that it was an anthology of children's poetry he was letting himself in for. By the same token I was rather more cautious, until I had contacted the poet, about work by older people submitted to me by parents and teachers. As I made this decision I prayed that there would be no children of eighty or even twenty-eight to consider; and in the event there was no-one older than eighteen, and only a very few entries from people as old as this.

I think that I was right and that the contributors were right and that my advisers were wrong. There were a number of factors, mostly concerned with the age of Sixth-

Form leavers. No-one would suppose that such an anthology should be geared to the unsynchronised and chronically ill-functioning machinery of British education; but it would be equally ridiculous to fancy that the leaving-age of the most intelligent sector of the population should have no bearing on the matter at all. I include poetry by people of eighteen not because the state system is there, but as a result of what it is. One result is that we have eighteen-year-old children in the country; and although none of my senior contributors strikes me as being in the least bit childish, their good voices exist in the context of the bad voices, and these latter, the rejects, seem all too often to have inherited badness rather than failed to achieve goodness. It is interesting to consider what the good voices have had to digest in order to become what they are. Perhaps fourteen was a significant age after all. Subsequently the liberal education in English becomes an obstacle race designed to trip everything except genius, but over which genius is automatically debarred from running.

Another result of the late leaving age is that there are poets of eighteen, real poets, who do not know the value of their own wares enough to send to magazines and publishers, but who have sent them to me instead. They are poets of maturity and significance who have been persuaded by the immature and insignificant people who teach them to think of themselves as children. How can we expect the writings of the young to be always vital and new when they are surrounded by so much death?

In most cases I have not published their poetry here, and for a variety of reasons, mainly instinctive. I hope that they will try elsewhere and go on trying, collecting rejection-slips and sharpening their own values against other people's disapproval.

The poems I have chosen may also be the work of people

who will go on writing, and in several cases the voice is individual enough for me strongly to hope so; but their poems have seemed to belong to this anthology for one of two reasons: either they have been expressive of a problem of adolescence, or their poetic texture has been the texture of adolescence. To this second group we can perhaps add those strangely formal poems which are also the product of this age-group: they are not raw, but only because the writer has been aware of his rawness and has developed an instinct of self-protection through embellishment.

It is, in fact, this need to illustrate the adolescent which has led me to extend the anthology thus far. Adolescent poetry does have a flavour which is individual and recognisable, and I think it is critically healthy that we learn to recognise it, if only so we can detect its voice when it is heard in the work of poets who we would not suppose in point of years to be adolescent. One of the dangers of an educational system which encourages immaturity in the young is that we all emerge from it blind to immaturity in the old, and we are especially blind to artistic immaturity. It is fashionable enough to be suspicious of Shelley and Swinburne on these grounds, and even to overlook the intellectual qualities and control over texture which should largely render them immune from such a suspicion. Why is it we do not spot in a flash the adolescent flavour of Eliot's *Marina*, for example? Is it because he is our Schoolmaster? M. la Rue's poem on page 86 is worth reading in this context, the more so since it seems to derive from *Marina*— only in this case the image has rather more flesh than the reality, probably because this area of association is more fertile during one's teens than later, and poetry with this richness of surface imagery is generally a product of a poet's early maturity. This is not to belittle an established poet by making elaborate claims on behalf of a newcomer, especially since, in this case, it was the established poet who created the imaginative precedent. What I am saying is that these two poems demarcate an important area of the imagination, and that it is profitable to consider which is the richer in texture, the genuine or the displaced adolescent. There is nothing new in observing that Eliot is a poet who repeatedly works against the bias of his imagination; this is just another instance of it. The adolescent poets whose works I have included seem to be working *along* the bias of their imagination at present, and this, of course, is a process which becomes harder as one grows older. For the moment what interests me is the nature of that imagination and the quality of its expression.

Susan Van Colle, for example, in her poem *Insensitive* makes a very accurate statement of a problem of adolescence and she uses the imagery of adolescence as well, and this sustained fusion of language and meaning makes hers one of the most interesting poems I have read. The poem ends:

> For you see I am young,
> (So he says)
> And narrowly shaded
> As a corner building in a crowded
> Street—but wait!
> I am not yet proven,
> And your eyes are not piercing
> Enough—your legs not supple enough
> To climb my walls. You are blind
> To me and all my standing.

What is interesting to me here, and there are similar examples in the *Daily Mirror's* book *Children As Writers* (3), is the *personal* feminine voice: there is a note here which few, if any, mature women poets possess. Most women who write poetry from a viewpoint which is recognisably feminine,

Kathleen Raine and Edith Sitwell, for example, are only feminine in the sense that the oracles were. They write from a cosmic conception of womanhood, not a personal one. This is a perfectly good note to aspire to, and it produces excellent poetry. The disappointing thing is that the women poets who do not write in this way rarely write as people, and one listens in vain for a voice which will present a feminine viewpoint without attitudinising. Some of the nineteenth century women poets were more uncompromising about their situation, of course; although it could be argued that at least two of them, Emily Bronte and Christina Rossetti, wrote from the vacuum of emotional immaturity. Is it in fact only the emotionally or intellectually immature woman who produces feminine poetry? If it is, then we must cherish her poems while we may. But in the body of this anthology the reader will find many poems which fit into a clear line of development from the Cleo Geary poem quoted earlier, written when its author was eight, and this poem by Susan Van Colle, written when she was sixteen. What happens to this voice? The woman artist always complains that Society does not want her to be feminine, and the answer is that Society does not want her to be bogus about being feminine, which is something quite different. Many of the poems here by girls are uncompromisingly feminine in viewpoint and idiom, and I find them fresh and exciting for that reason. Perhaps this is a new trend, but I doubt it. I doubt if there is an imaginative evolution from generation to generation. No doubt we are seeing what always happened, only people have not always been concerned to see it.

*　　*　　*

It is worth pursuing this idea a little further, because it involves the whole educational and creative problem of disappearing talent.

Girls' poetry encompasses a far greater range than boys' poetry, not in subject matter, certainly, but in style; and at its best it is often more complex and penetrating, even if less flamboyant than boys'. It ranges between the most mannered or the most transparent of personal idioms and the most blatantly and slavishly derivative; and it is not unusual to find the work of the same girl fluctuating violently between these poles, though rarely within the space of a single poem— unlike some boys' poetry, because girls in general have a greater sensitivity and control over the individual poem.

It is this lack of polarity which destroys the feminine voice, and which in the end destroys the growth of most children as writers. The greater the sensitivity the greater, paradoxically, the desire to imitate, at least in immaturity. The greater the control over the individual utterance, then obviously the greater the immediate stylistic harmony for the job in hand, but the lesser the tension which will forge and polarise a style for permanent use. Most girls find the easy answer sooner than most boys, but in any case both of them find it too soon. This explains the absence of tension I complained of earlier; and it also reinforces the statement that it is irrelevant to see the products of a creative education as part of the progress of our culture: they are merely a process in it.

Indeed, in our current treatment of child art we are the guilty victims of a number of historical fallacies, as is inevitable in any age which fancies it has uncovered the major educational truths.

One of these fallacies is that we live in an age of imaginative liberation for the young, following on many centuries of imaginative repression. Our creative education in the Arts, the implication is, has at last been able to tap the eternal pulse; we have discovered the dynamic which will see mankind through for ever.

The historian always smiles at the educator, but the latter never seems to notice, especially now he has the psychologist to persuade him that the Arts, and by inference, education, are in contact with processes which lie beyond history.

The voice of the modern child, we are told, is the true voice; it is the voice of the child eternal. Certainly it can sometimes be a very wonderful voice, as in this poem by Kenneth Ash:

> Trains are snorting monsters
> Running on snaky railway lines.
>
> An express train at night is like a jewelled snake,
> Writhing round the curves in the track.
>
> A goods train is like a line of dirty men,
> Plodding home after a good day's work.
>
> But I like trains.

Often, indeed, it is far more the best of all voices, as in this poem by a ten-year-old West Indian girl called Lucky Cadogan:

> When can I fly by myself
> Mother dear?
> Now, Billy dear.
>
> Hurrah! Now the time has come
> When I can play
> And scatter yellow pollen
> For fun.
>
> Play is not what God wants us to do
> My boy, Billy dear.

The educator who fancies, probably mistakenly, that his

was the influence responsible for this fine expression of freedom can perhaps be forgiven if he sounds somewhat cock-a-hoop. If only the dead could have found out in time!

Unfortunately there is no evidence to support the idea that the young always could have been like this if only their elders and betters would have let them, and that the imagination of, say, the Victorian child was only half developed because all of this was repressed. Indeed, there is some evidence to the contrary. It is true that we have forged new keys to unlock new doors, but I fancy that most of the rooms were empty until we walked into them.

What we have discovered to be repressed has a curiously modern flavour, and the young were not always modern; they were merely contemporary: they were the unselective sponges of all that was superficial to their age. In an over-selective era like the early eighteenth century their progress to artistic maturity would have been an especially difficult one. There is nothing we could have done to make it any easier.

If we are right now, it is only in a transitory sense. We may appear to ourselves to better for our children, but this is probably the result of living in an age which has reorientated itself towards the primitive in art and the psychotic in imagination. We have seen youth and age divided not by a ladder but by a barrier, and we have knocked that obstacle down. But there was a time when the ladder was truer, and it may become our image again. It is just possible that in a book of this sort we may be able to glimpse what the rungs of that ladder should be. For the moment it is a sobering thought that the ease with which children become adult today may be merely because the adults are culturally so like their children.

*　　*　　*

People who disapprove of the idea of children being encouraged as creative writers often complain about the absence of intellect and control displayed in their work. This is scarcely a valid criticism, especially of what is generally regarded to be a complementary rather than an alternative activity, and it is even less valid in an age whose adult culture is equally barren of these qualities.

It is always very difficult to demonstrate the intellectual calibre of a good piece of creative writing, because the wit never walks naked, and this is perhaps why so many of the analytical critics are so bad at discovering what is good in the new; but if we are prepared to see intellect in the ability to control the presentation of an experience, and the creative intelligence at work in the delicate probing of that experience, then I think it is possible to refute the criticism on its own grounds. There are a number of excellent poems in the section entitled *The Ego Alone And Lost* (a phrase taken from one of them) which seem to me to be unusually sensitive and well-formed by any standards: *Quis?*, *The Painter*, *Mother*, *The Gallery*, are just a few of the examples the reader may care to consider in this context. Here is *The Gallery* by Jacqueline Trievnor, written when she was fourteen:

> The gallery with its padded chairs
> Stark and bare,
> The faces in the pictures
> Incapable of human thought
> Stared at me.
> They looked hard at me
> As if to penetrate my innermost feelings
> And make me one of them.
> It unnerved me;
> I wanted to escape

But I was paralysed
Until a small boy pointed at one of the pictures
And laughed.

What the young poet is less good at, save when being purely imitative, is dealing with the generalised experience. He is unhappy with social or sociological comment, for example. In *The Life And the Soul of the Party*, which is a poem I enjoy, the protest is in personal terms; we see not so much the bore as the boredom and the contempt; and in a poem like *Campbell Street*, which is printed in another section of the anthology, the compulsion seems a literary rather than an emotional one.

Very rare indeed is the note struck by Peter Tinsley in a poem called *Please Keep Off The Grass:*

A democratic state, they said,
A democratic land.
They printed little gold-edged notes
And hired a silver band.
You may say what you like, they said,
If you do as you're told,
So please keep off the grass, my friend,
In case the grass is sold.

This poem was written when the author was thirteen; and it, and others by him, succeed in being the exception for a rather significant reason. Like the poems by Michael Thompson in a younger age-group, they are part of a considerable body of verse produced by their author over a number of years. Poetry, even when it is the work of primitives and children, needs practice. The individual poem may flourish, it may be an important personal and educational experience, and it may, as do many poems in this volume, give delight; but an anthology of poems which are not the products of a sustained interest and intention must accept certain limitations.

One of these is that it can offer very little evidence about the stamina of the average child writer. Most children, even when they are in a richly creative environment, progress very rapidly through a variety of imaginative phases, and it is only in one or two of these that poetry seems to flourish. Most teachers only see a child's work over a brief period of time, and there is no evidence to show that creating poetry, valuable though it is at the right point of development, is capable of being a continuous process for more than a very few children. In *Poetry Without Tears*, although I urge and would continue to urge the writing of verse during all of the educational stages, there is an acceptance of the fact that for many of them it is verse and only verse which is being written.

In the case of those few children who do go on writing poetry, that is who make a serious attempt at self-expression in verse over a number of years—and their incidence is sufficiently infrequent to make us wonder whether we are not witnessing the genesis of the adult poet, or the premature development and collapse of the potential poet—one of the currently unpalatable truths that emerges is this. Stamina depends upon or at least includes the ability to digest form and literary influences. As C. Day Lewis remarks in his preface to a collection of undergraduate poetry, genuine talent frequently hides itself until late in parody and imitation.

This fact has always been recognised, but for the wrong reasons and by the wrong people. It is the argument of those who oppose creative work in the arts; but I think those of us who favour such work should not close our eyes to the essential truth of this part of the opposition's case. Some of us are carrying so big a banner that we cannot always see where we are leading the band. Then when the procession is lost up the alley we drop it and run.

Surely we favour the free creation of poetry at certain stages because it does most children most good and does nothing to harm the remainder. We must not try to make our educational processes do more than they can; we must not try to incorporate a literary scaffolding on the basis of copying the growth of those who display creative stamina. To do so would be to act on the basic fallacy, evidently deeply rooted in the minds of some of those who believe in a creative education, that it lies within our ability to teach all the young to be creative in their maturity. In fact, it should be our hope that a few more of them will grow up, as a result of what we have done and of what they have done, to be more sensitively appreciative of the world around them. The making of the poems in this anthology will have been a small germ of growth for each of the authors, the more so since they have been sufficiently talented to produce work which makes a valid shape from their perceptions.

An unpleasant carollary to this, and it applies to the anthologist as well as the teacher, is that if we do encounter the creative writer of the future we shall probably be unable to recognise him. He will pretty certainly write a lot of dull verse and resist our attempts to make him brighter; and this latency rather than evidency of talent will be in addition to the fact that most of us, as today's teachers, are quite incapable on critical grounds of recognising tomorrow's genius.

This is not a digression. What we do in our creative work with children depends not upon our sense of tomorrow but on our passion for here and now. Most of the major fallacies are based upon our neurotic concern for the unknown dimension of the future; we are forever prescribing as a result of prognosis instead of basing our treatment on our perception of today.

* * *

And so, with the best will in the world, the thesis becomes an educational one; and this is surely just, because the poetry of emergent individualism is finally an educational rather than an artistic phenomenon. But its validity for us, as I said earlier, is more than this. The thesis rests upon the poetry, not the other way about, and the poetry, even if it is excellence in isolation, is good enough to kindle our enthusiasm. If we look at it not as educators, not as critics, but as people who have an interested concern for the processes of contemporary culture—a verbose way of saying general readers—then we will find a great deal here to commend.

Because, finally, I have hesitated so much and qualified so many praises not because I think the poetry is not good enough, but because I think it is so good that it may be judged in a misleading context, and that much of it may emerge from that context with credit.

If it is credit for the poetry, well and good; it is the relationship between the poem and the poet that is sometimes to be questioned. Poets talk of inspiration, and there is inspiration in the following pages in plenty; but the inspiration of the mature poet, although it cannot always be controlled, can be conditioned by preference. A poet exercises choice over his imaginative impulses, and is also made free by experience to reject what he finds in them. What these poems lack, since their excellence is not in most cases a part in a sequence of excellence, is just this quality of choice and rejection. Ability is only the beginning.

Just how significant a beginning the reader will have ample opportunity to judge; and as he does so I hope he will be able to remember, as I have had to, the parents and teachers and nameless encouragers of the poets who have not only exercised this quality of choice on their behalf by opening up fresh areas of experience, but who have done even more for them by quite simply caring.

I paid tribute to these people, the educators, at the beginning, when I used the phrase 'second-hand'. What I meant, in an age not generally considered to be more than apathetic in its approach to poetry and to education through the arts, can be seen if I mention the two thousand individual responses received as a result of an appeal in the press when the compilation of the anthology was well under way, many dozens of them being batches of fifty poems and above typed for me by teachers; it can be seen in the numerous instances that came to light of parents who had kept intelligently edited symposia of the works of their children, not always in homes that one would have expected to have a background of culture; it can be seen from the numerous magnificently produced school magazines and collections sent to me, and from the anthologies compiled by School-Groups and Associations and Local Education Authorities. I think it can be seen in a hundred other individual instances, exemplified for me by the undergraduate who sent me the work of Lucky Cadogan, the West Indian girl he had taught while on supply. Because, appropriately, her poetry displayed qualities which went beyond the doubts and the confusion of values and touched almost on the mystery:

From a bright summers day
The sky turns grey
Then as I look upward
I see diamonds falling
From a heavenly plane.

Downwards they fall, feeding
The land,
Kissing one
Anothers hand.

There we have the tradition and the truth and the

spontaneity. It may be only the tradition that endures for a month, but for that month the language is charged by the ceaseless regeneration of childhood.

> But the black case of jewels
> No more throws out its treasure
> But gathers them up.
> I look down,
> The world is silent.

A Gallery

Orgy, the Psycho

with no hard feelings for Sir Patrick Spens

The beat pads out in Coney Isle
    With his meths instead of wine;
'Man, where will I git a crazy drummer
    To jazz in this band o' mine?'

So up and spat a real cool chick,
    Sat at the hipster's knee,
'Orgy the Psycho's the coolest squelch
    That ever I did see'.

Dear Daddy-O, Dear Daddy-O,
    Dear Daddy-O, in yer pad,
Like a hipster chick from Soho
    Digs bands that swing her trad.

We got big eyes for yer bongo drums
   And yer hep-cat jazzin' beat,
We dig you for our combo,
   To make it kind o' neat.

So the beat arrived at the party,
   Complete with his set of drums,
Dug himself in with the coolest chick
   And sneered at all us bums.

They hadna played a beat, a beat,
   A beat but barely three,
When the chicks got swingin' and the beats got singin'
   An hips jived crazily.

Half hour, half hour till this beat got sour,
   An' bugged himself into a fight,
He cracked a bottle over a stiff
   An' laid him out all night.

Now, man, there came a sly blue nik,
   A fake sent by the cops,
We hitched this, like he'd had a bath
   And shaved around his chops.

He'd come to nab the woozy hips,
   Like Orgy the Psycho too,
But laith, laith were our crazy heps
   To part with the junk they chew.

But lang, lang may the cool chicks sit,
   For it's five years each they keep;
And there pads Orgy the Psycho
   Wi' the cool heps at his feet.

D. GOSLING

The Dirty Old Woman

On the way to School
    I see a dirty old woman.
She ill-treats her pets.
    I see a dirty old woman
And never washes.
    I see a dirty old woman
She has a dog, but never brushes it.
    Horrid old woman.
Dirty old woman.

You won't like her when you see her
    Dirty old woman,
I see her nearly every day
    And makes me feel sick
Dirty old woman.

SUSAN BARTER

The Old Tramp

With eyes like saucers
Full of grief and pity,
With a heart full of sorrow,
And a soul of anguish.
With clothes of green,
All tattered and torn,
A hat of blue,
And shoes of brown,
This was the tramp.

His hands were chapped,
His arms were bare and cold,
His face was haggard,
And he was small and stout,
With a nose like a button,
All red with cold;
The blue hat of his
Had a bird's nest in,
This was the tramp.

HELOISE MAHOOD

The Tie

My Daddy has a tie,
　Can you tell me why?
To put around his neck, of course,
　Just like a halter round a horse.

LYNNE WILKINSON

A Reflection in a Mirror

The reflection,
It is of a beautiful woman
With golden streaks in her hair.

She had red lips,
As red as the blood of a man
Her eyes,
They were blue green
The colour of the Atlantic Ocean.

She was vain,
With comb in one hand, and brush in the other
She looked in the mirror from one hour to another.

JACQUELINE ELDRIDGE

Boys

Boys are nasty, dirty and mean.
Girls are beautiful, slim and clean.
Boys slam desk-tops and classroom doors,
They never think of school rules and laws.
When going home,
They thump each other.
When at home,
They try their mother.
They never seem to clean their nails;
Boys should wear curly tails
And have a snubby, grunting nose,
Flappy ears and 'trotter' toes.

S. ROBINSON

Old Grey One

You—old grey one
    Old and wizened in age.
You, whom the sun
    Has yellowed and faded.
You, with your pale eyes
    Made dim and shaded.

You, with slow steps,
  And even slower mind.
Loose mumbling lips
  That croak in voice low-toned.
You, a thing decayed,
  With your hands witch-boned.

You, who sleep now—
  Mouth open, fitfully.
Your dry, lined brow,
  And thin sparse locks of hair.
Your blue-veined parchment skin,
  You, with vacant stare.

You—old grey one,
  Have you no memory
Of youth, so long gone?
  And were you a wife?
No other heart but yours?
  O tell me the story of life!

PATRICIA BROWNING

Saturdays

On Saturdays I play with my brother
A cheerful little chap
So gaily he plays digging away
Tries to get the tadpoles in the Oxo tin,
Pokes the dog's eyes and pulls his tail

He gets in the coke and his face gets black
He goes in the barn and tries to ride the bike,
He picks the flowers and squashes them in his hand
And watches the bumble bees getting the honey.

SHERON FREER

The Old Sailor's Stories

The Old Sailor sits on the quay,
  The sea all around him glistening;
And when I go down he talks to me
  And I sit on the quayside listening.

He told me he captained sailing ships
  With cargoes of fruit and cotton;
The journeys he made weren't pleasure trips
  When the food for the crew went rotten.

He told me stories of storms and gale
  With sea breaking open the hatches;
Sometimes it makes my face turn pale
  To think of those long, lone watches.

N. GAGEN

Limericks

A young English student named Thomas
Confused all his colons and commas.
At the past simple tense
He was exceedingly dense,
And his future did not hold much promise.

VALERIE ADAMS

There was a young lady of Italy
Who sang in a manner quite prettily
A mad gondolier
Shook his fist in her ear,
'You're drowning my song', he said bitterly.

ROWENA MILLS

A violin said to a 'cello,
'Your voice is exceedingly mellow;
My fiddling soprano
Sounds pretty piano,
By your very fortissimo bellow'.

SARAH BROWN

Three Clerihews

Hereward the Wake,
Dived into the lake.
He got a thorough wetting
Now his hair needs setting.

WENDY SHIRLEY

Anne of Cleves
Wore puffed sleeves,
And she stuck in the door
For an hour or more.

MARGARET SCAIFE

King Arthur and his Knights,
Set out to fly their kites;
Because of too much breeze,
The kites caught on the trees.

RUTH WILLIAMS

Great Aunts

Laces and frills are what they wear,
And sometimes petticoats with just a slight tear;
Spectacles perched on the end of her nose,
A walking stick tapping away as she goes,
Sneezes and coughs and strong scented hanks,
Signs of disgust when told of school pranks.
Everyone's called either 'dear', or 'my dear',
She will NEVER consent to a brilliant idea,
Fusses and bothers are not to be mentioned,
She talks of her nephew and where he was stationed.
When driving her car she may lose her nerves,
She drives well on the straight, but can't manage curves;
She still has no licence—it's the police she fears—
But as I can see, she'll go on for years!

ANN GOULD

My Grandma

A friendly old lady
With silvery hair
Her face is now wrinkled
But once she was fair

She lies on the bed
So weary is she
But still I do love her
And hope she loves me.

My Aunts

I've an aunt in Canada, she's called Aunt Jane,
She's short and thin, and ever so plain,
But sometimes she's different, and forgets she's grown up,
She romps and she squeals just like a young pup.

And Sarah, she lives down South,
She's fat and jolly, with a round, rosy mouth,
She's got six children, all grown up and wed,
And my Aunt Sarah makes ginger-nut bread.

Aunt Molly, shes' almost fifty or so,
She lives in—oh, I don't know,
She has two children called Jennie and Jim,
Aunt Molly is jolly, and neither fat nor thin.

There—you've heard of my aunts—all jolly,
Aunt Sarah, Aunt Jane, and Aunt Molly,
Who live in Canada, Down South, and—I've forgotten
    again,
But I know if I changed them, I'd be really insane.

B. GREENWOOD

36

The Ballad of Timothy Tibbits

When young Timothy Tibbits decided to wed,
    With a Flumpety, Tooliboots, Puck.
'I shall search 'till I find a sweet maiden,' he said,
'Whose hair is spun gold, and whose lips are sweet red,
And I vow I will love her until I am dead.'
    With a Flumpety, Tooliboots, Puck.

So he saddled his horse, and he made up his pack.
    With a Flumpety, Tooliboots, Puck.
And his mother said, 'Woe!' and 'Alas!' and 'Alack!'
'If he goes away now with his horse and his sack,
What a useless young beauty is sure to come back.'
    With a Flumpety, Tooliboots, Puck.

Young Timothy wandered through village and town.
    With a Flumpety, Tooliboots, Puck.
'Till the leaves on the trees turned from green to red-brown,
As he spurned first that face, then this hair, then that gown,
And his poor troubled brow wore a permanent frown.
    With a Flumpety, Tooliboots, Puck.

So, wearily, Timothy came to an inn.
    With a Flumpety, Tooliboots, Puck.
And a plump, buxom maiden said, 'My! What a sin,
That a handsome young gentleman grows pale and thin,
For lack of a maiden to woo and to win.'
    With a Flumpety, Tooliboots, Puck.

So she baked and she cooked, and she tended him well.
    With a Flumpety, Tooliboots, Puck.
Till her raven-black locks, and her laugh like a bell,
Made him gay, blithe, and cheerful, and so it befell,
That he loved her, and wed her, I'm happy to tell.
    With a Flumpety, Tooliboots, Puck.

VIVIENNE GOULT

A Long Walk

One day a woman said that she
Would show how pleasant a walk could be,
The walk was nearly a thousand miles
But that is nothing if done with smiles.

So off she set on this very long trek,
But would she finish a walking wreck?
Would she be full of the joys of spring
When she had finished this journeying?

She tramped and trekked from morn till night
On carrot leaves and things as light.
Some said 'she's mad,' but I don't know
She set the fashion for others to go.

Her name was Doctor Barbara Moore,
Perhaps you've heard that name before,
Or do you think of the second lot
Whose interest lay in the money pot.

A pound was earned with every mile
You might think it was worth while,
But no amount of one pound notes
Would make me walk from John o' Groats.

C. SIMONDS

Jane, Do Be Careful

'Oh, Jane, do be careful!
You've spilt the milk
You've drowned the cat,
Jane, do be careful.

'Oh, Jane, do be careful!
   Look at that ink
   In the dog's drink.
Jane, do be careful.

'Oh, Jane, do be careful!
   You spend money galore
   It makes your dad sore,
Jane, do be careful.

'Oh, Jane, do be careful!
   You'll sorrow for this
   You'll sorrow for that,
Jane, do be careful.

IRENE PAGE

Tommy

Tommy, Tommy, where can he be?
He has gone to the deep blue sea.
   Tommy, Tommy, do not drown.
Or I'll never see you in town.

CELIA WALKER

Sir Walter Raleigh

Sir Walter Raleigh
On a venturesome sally,
Grovelled in the mud
And found the common spud.

JULIA HALL

Topsy Turvey

If I had hands upon my head,
I'd walk upside down instead,
I'd see the world all upside down,
And be the funniest boy in town,
It would not be much use to me,
I like the world as it is, you see.

CHRISTOPHER FISHER

God Bless

A little boy kneels at the foot of the bed
Saying his evening prayers.
'Dear God, please will you tell my mummy
I'm sorry I pushed her downstairs.
And if my auntie's up there with you
Will you please tell her I'm sorry too,
I didn't know that she would die
If I put poison in the pie,
About the man in the bowler hat,
I didn't mean to shoot his cat.
Sister Jane has gone away
All because she wouldn't play,
I weighed her down with great big rocks
And put her in a wooden box
And then I pushed it in the sea.
I don't think she came home to tea.
And God, I'm really awfully sorry
I pushed poor Charlie under a lorry.
So God bless anyone alive,
It's time, I think, I learnt to drive.'

PETER TINSLEY

Birds and Beasts

Baby Jumbo

Baby Jumbo is chubby and fat,
He's four feet fat or fatter than that.
Five feet tall is his length,
He carries six ton to show his strength.

Pink is his colour,
The same as his mother,
Blue are his eyes,
The colour of the skies.

BELINDA GOULD

Polar Bear

Polar bear, tell me
Why sleep on ice blocks?
Why not sleep on beds like we do?
Why hang over a hole?
Why not fish with a line?
I like your fur coat, soft as could be.
Why not give away your coat?
Give it to the people like me.

CHRISTOPHER RICHARDS

The Lion

A golden lion
With fur as smooth as softest silk
And eyes like great dark pools;
A lion made of gold and silver,
Curved silver claws and golden fur;
A lion dead as the darkest night.

His shaggy head lay on two velvet paws,
His body dead and cold
Motionless in the silver moonlight,
Dead as the darkest night.

JANE HORLOCK

Garden Scene

He stood upon a brick,
Eyes glinting Death,
Strutted between the twig and broken stick,
Pride vaulting in his breast at every breath,
Staccato, jerky, strides and ruffled tail
And vicious beak that seized a limping snail.

The crack of shell on stone
Echoed from trees,
Life splintered, and with low, despairing moan
Was borne away by some funereal breeze
And ebbed along the ribbed, white shores of Spite,
To vanish into haunted fields of Night.

ANTHONY EVANS

The Owl

Twit, twoo,
Twit, twa-a.
Who are you?
Don't ask who I are.
Gr-growl
Gr-growl
He's a nuisance,
That old owl.

DIANA FERGUSON

The Dead Bird

Once a free, winged arrow throbbing with life,
Now a heap of bone and feather.
Wet, bedraggled, windblown,
The bird lies, its body growing cold,
Colour fading, eyes dim.
Just an object of pity.
Shot.
Shot for no reason at all,
One quick action ended its wasted life.

D. GILES

The Little Bird

There was a little bird
What goes twinkling in the trees,
And every time you look at him
He twinkles back at you.
And that is the end of the story.

TONY

Escape

Escape, free at last,
Looked out, no sound,
Remembered the past,
And shuddered.

'Why shut me in?
Inside this prison,
For no known sin—
Now free!

At last I have my say,
Away from bars.'
Free now; and away
The parrot fluttered.

S. CARDY

If I Was a Dog

If I was a dog,
I wouldn't bark all day,
 I would wait for a cat
  To chase away.

If I was a cat,
I wouldn't meaow all day,
 I would wait for a mouse
  To chase away.

DIANE FURGUSON

The Millipede

The millipede has struck a hitch,
Deciding which foot goes with which.
You bipeds should not just condemn her,
But pity her, in her dilemma.

ANGELA SIMMONS

The Hedgehog

Projecting prickles
  Speared leaves,
Inquiring eyes—shadowing
  A whiskery snout;
Minute feet,
  Curved claws
Scratched the soil . . .
  An armoured hedgehog scrambled out.

Wrinkled nose
  Sniffed the air,
Feet propelled—towards
  The grey wall;
Little beetle
  Ran away . . .
Leaf fell, hedgehog
  Curled tightly in a ball.

Snout appeared,
  Eyes blinked,
Legs began—forward
  Cautiously to creep;
Enormous hole—
  Plonk!
Hedgehog fell,
  Rolled, and went to sleep.

ROSEMARY PHILLIPS

The Dead Cat

As I was walking along the road
I heard the church bells ringing
Then I looked up at a tree
And heard a little bird singing
As I looked down on to the road
I saw a dead cat lying
Everything seemed to be happy
Except the dead cat lying.

SHEILA STEWART

A Fox Cub

In the pine trees on the hill
There is an old foxes' lair.
A new family live in it now:
Cubs not very old with the vixen and the dog.
In the shade of those trees
I listen.
The cubs come out and look around.
A shot!
One shot!
A howl, a painful howl.
I look and see a cub writhing in agony on the ground.
I run to it, I pick it up,
I take it home and look after it.
It grows up, I set it free.
It bounds up the hill to the pines,
To its old home.
So once again the red russet streak
Of a fox's run for life

Will show against the moonlight,
As it bounds towards the old, old home of foxes
In the pine trees on the hill.

ANN LOVELL

The Little Fox

Sport?
The little fox and I have other names.

'You will enjoy it', said my friend,
'Come with me—I have a horse
I'll lend it'. So I went . . .
So I came—waiting in excitement.
No shame.

The fox away!
We fly! start nag! start!
Or I'll be left behind. . . .
The hounds bay!
The Fox. . . ?

The little beast—afraid—
Breaks loose from sheltered bush;
The hounds. . . .

The fox breaks away and dodges
Here and there . . . he doubles
Back again. Now crouches
Watching, panting—off again.
No resting—sleep—just fear
Blind fear, cold fear,
The hounds. . . .

The hounds are near, they howl,
The scent is warm in their nostrils—
Dilated, the fox runs into cover.
Sanctuary?

The hounds are near. The fox,
Exhausted, has died a thousand deaths,
Before he turns to face the hounds,
Gladly! No fear now, no fight,
Too gone to care.

Teeth clench, teeth open, teeth snap,
A squeal, one squeal to rend
The hearts of men more tough than I,
Snarling—growling—tearing—rending—
Blood spurts. . . .

Don't stand and stare!
Oh God! must stop this awful thing.
Forward! forward! quickly mare!
Too late—man clothed in coat
Like the blood on the ground—draws knife,
Picks up the little fox, pitiful, dreadful,
Mangled sight. . . .

Cuts off the brush, the little body
Drops to the ground.

He holds up the brush with pride,
Blood drips down—must turn away—
Feel sick—must hide.

Sport?
The little fox and I have other names.

VALERIE WOOD

The Fox

With cunning eye
And sleek brown coat.
Over the fields so sly—
White-tipped brush,
There he goes
Over grass so soft.
His ears pricked up,
Over marsh and bog
To his earth he speeds
Safe from man and dog.

RACHEL WHITE

On Seeing a Fox Skull

'A skull, a skull!' cried a girl,
' 'Tis a fox skull, it's not alive.
Lying dead and alone,
With long and short teeth still white as snow.
Smooth and rough the skull appears:
With eye holes, nose hole too,
But without the eyes, nose and ears,
And the flesh of former years'.

LYNN TAYLOR

The Battle

The snake slithers through the grass,
Stops, listens, raising its head.
Slides on slowly.
The evening is coming.
The snake raises its head again;
Its tongue flits in and out;
Hissing breaks the silence.
The enemy shows itself—
It is a wolf!
The wolf advances, cautiously,
The snake rears.
The wolf leaps and the battle commences.
The snake strikes quickly, hissing.
The wolf dies.
The snake is triumphant
But it is wounded.
It tries to heal its wounds, but dies.
Bees buzz over the bodies, lying in the snow,
Dancing over the bodies till dusk falls.

KEVIN CAMPBELL

The Snake

In the mysterious undergrowth,
Animals lie.
Among them is the snake,
His long coils
Sparkling in the sun
As he twists himself around a tree trunk.

His sharp glittering eyes darting
Like arrows.
Searching the ground for prey.
He watches and waits.
Then as quick as a fork of lightning,
His forked tongue shoots out
And his meal is caught.

SYLVIA WEARING

The Frog and the Log

Said a frog on a log,
'Listen, little bunny—
Will you ride by my side?
Wouldn't that be funny?'

PAMELA MARSHALL

Lucky Black Cat

Oh lucky black cat with fur so soft,
How brightly your eyes do gleam!
All through the night by candlelight
Opalescent they flash blue and green.

Your mistress is an awful witch,
Day long by her pot she stands.
To stir the bubbling liquid, which
Is the colour of her hands.

Her cave is lined with long brown shelves
Where her ugly spell-book stands.
Around the walls hang great black bells,
Patterned with bright gold bands.

Oh quiet black cat with fur so soft,
In a very strange world you dwell,
Nevermore will I stroke your silky coat,
For I fear you might cast a spell.

EILEEN ARRANDALE and
IMELDA PAYNE.

Sandy, My Pussy

Sandy the pussy has got a sore head,
Sandy the pussy has gone to bed,
Sandy the pussy told me why—
He fell in the washing-machine
    And was spun-dry.

E. HARRISON

Cats

Cats,
Are like a ball of wool, rolling down a hillside,
When cats are at play,
You feel as if a lion is chasing you
Through a paradise of tables and chairs.

Cats,
When angry, are like a dragon,
Burning you with his fiery tongue;
But if you fight back:
It pangs your heart,
For you love the creature really.

A. BARNARD

The Dove and the Wren

The dove says, 'Coo,
What shall I do?
I can hardly keep my two!'
'Pooh,' says the wren.
'Why I've got ten,
And I keep them all
Like gentlemen!'

PAMELA MARSHALL

The Flamingo

A cloud of white and pink
Flocked to the river bank;
The cloud went down and almost sank.

The graceful, sweeping walk,
The graceful, stretching necks,
The gentle, little pecks.

They bent their heads together
And picked the fish.
Then with one soft swish,
The pink and white moulded feathers
Had gone!

JEANNE POOK

The Fish

I saw a fish in a river,
   It did look sweet.
I thought I'd have it for dinner,
   But the fish said, 'Wouldn't
     You rather have meat?'

JUNE CRABTREE

Rats

At the bottom of our garden their is a little stream
It is fast running where it's shallow,
But where it's deep it is almost still.
The bank is made of soft clay
In which the rats nest.
They clamber up the bank
Into the people's gardens;
They raid the eggs of nesting birds.
We have watched them climb quite high in trees.
There is a certain beauty in them while they are alive,
But when they are dead that beauty disappears,
Their heads are limp and they are quite still,
Still and silent.

NANNETTE COLLEEN BURT

White Snow

White snow,
  White snow,
    Tortoise underneath,
Robin looking for his nest
  While the winter creeps.

SUSAN YOUNG

The Tree Creeper

The wee bird
Creeping up the tree
Never even heard
Or saw me.

ALISON BRITTON

The Thief of Linkfield Lane

There is a thief in Linkfield Lane,
  Who visits us each morning.
To Gran and me its very plain
  He thinks we're still a'yawning.

The milkman brings us bottles three,
  With yellow tops a'gleaming,
And watchful waiting on a tree
  The little thief sits scheming.

60

He pecks one bottle top away,
    Then he drinks the cream with glee;
We wondered if it was a jay,
    And planned one morn, we'd see.

We found that we could get a view
    From pantry window sighting,
And saw it was a tit so blue
    It really was exciting.

We've found the thief in Linkfield Lane
    Who visits us each morning.
To Gran and me it's very plain
    He'll always think we're yawning.

P. BRISEBOIS

The Prince's Steed

The Prince's Steed

The Prince's steed awaits him
On the cobbly path,
Legs straight, neck arched,
Standing under the marble arch.

His mane and tail like silver,
Against his golden hide,
Magnificent with his head held high,
Waiting for a ride.

His hoofs are like glass knives,
His sparkling wicked eyes
Glittering like diamonds,
As they ride across the skies.

As he gallops across the clouds
He sends a high-pitched neigh
Cantering amongst the brilliant stars.
He'll be back next day.

MAUREEN HUMPHRIES

Blow Me Down

Sharks and Swordfish dancing reels,
And monkeys biting fleas,
Pink and green and purple pigs
A-swinging in the trees.

Armadillos chewing steaks,
And tigers grinding corn,
Guinea pigs with tails so long
A-beating on the lawn.

Dogs with multi-coloured tails,
Crabs with little nippers,
Blue-nosed whales in uniform
A-wearing purple slippers.

All these things and many more,
Such fascinating scenes
Keep occurring every day—
I see them in my dreams.

JUDITH FAWCETT

The Dove

The leaves shudder
With a whisper of the unknown;
And excited quiver
Passes over the Earth,
The dove seeks refuge
In the safety of her cote,

She tries to rest
But emotion stirs within her,
Agitation for the calm
After the storm.
The crashes ring out,
The skies seem to be aflame;
The very heavens are rent
By the continuous roar of thunder.
It seems that all Creation
Will be torn asunder.
The torrents gush forth,
Freshening the parched earth.
Now the storm subsides,
The dove emerges
Serene and beautiful
Against the dark skies.
She flutters away,
As one day the great dove,
Shall sally forth to her destiny,
Unmoved by past terrors,
And no more
Shall storms shadow the Earth.

ELIZABETH SUTCLIFFE

Billy Bee

When can I fly by myself
Mother dear?
Not yet but when winter is clear

I would love to scatter
Yellow pollen to and fro
And sing in Mary's garden
Below.

When can I fly by myself
Mother dear?
Now, Billy dear.

Hurrah! Now the time has come
When I can play
And scatter yellow pollen
For fun.

Play is not what God wants us to do
My boy, Billy, dear.

LUCKY CADOGAN

The Dance

Out from a grave
Did a skeleton step
To Dance the night away
As he twisted and turned
And he danced about
His bones did joggle
And rattle about
All through the night
He danced away
Jiggle and joggle
He skipped about
Never a care
To think about

68

Jiggle and joggle
The whole night through
Till the cockerel crew
A morning new
How sad he was
To leave the earth
One more look
And the grave
Slammed shut.

CLEO GEARY

The Guardians of Night

The moon glides over the earth like a polished coin,
And sheds her cloak of translucency
Over a country swathed in snow.

The church, in an aura of bitter frostiness of fiery
    white icicles,
Projects white moss
Crevaced between drunken stones
In white lane togas of snow that hang in folds,
And the pinnacled stalagmite of the spire cuts into the
    black pane of night sky.

The pale light traces sweeping lines that artists dream of
Over gravestones
Like sugar loaves of irridescent magic
And sheds icy-cool mystery on spangled sequined stones
And depths of dreamy blue
And throws blue shadows of dusky froth on aloof
    grey palings.

69

The trees, black and spiky, maliciously prick the
    radiant beams of light.
Crystalline branches weave intricate silver patterns
Against the unblemished blackness
While uncovered bark glistens like black opals
And phosphorescent ice, like a petrol stream, slides off
    slippery branches.

The moon retreats behind bluish vapour
And leaves the world to shadows.

JOY THOMPSON

In Days of Old

In days of old
The knights were bold
(Or so we're told).

And every day
Would dragons slay
(Or so they'd say),

And maidens fair
With flowery hair
Save from despair.

And armour clad,
With helm and flag,
Did joust and brag.

But knights today
No longer play
And dragons slay;

And maidens fair
Now take their share
Of toil and care.

Now in this land
The ladies stand
While men do sit
And sometimes knit;
'Tis plain to see
That chivalry
Is not to be.

R. A. W. COX

Rain

From a bright summer's day
The sky turns grey
  Then as I look upwards
    I see diamonds falling
      From a heavenly plane.

Downwards they fall, feeding
      The land,
  Kissing one
    Anothers hand.

But the black case of jewels
No more throws out its treasures
      But gathers them up.
        I look down,
      The world is silent.

LUCKY CADOGAN

The Modern Way

O come with me and see the moon,
If we have time we'll visit Mars,
It's really quite a pleasant trip,
Great fun at night with all the stars
That shine like diamonds in the sky.

Please say you'll come,
It won't take long.
My Rocket's waiting just outside.
I've passed my test with perfect ease,
And long to take you for a ride.

JACQUELINE NEWMAN

Space Travel

It won't be long before we catch
A rocket up to Mars
And spend the weekend visiting
Our friends upon the stars.
At Christmas when the days are cold
And the carol singers sing
We'll catch a rocket round the sun
And get a taste of Spring.

J. POWELL

The Cupboard Under the Stairs

I groped in the dark,
And blundered like a bat or a bee
Into two creaking baskets on their hooks.

I groped again,
And clasped the smooth ring-handle
Of the lamp which was covered with dust and grey-green
     roughnesses

I switched it on.
Clear moonlight shone through the frosted glass
But still creepy shadows lurked in the farthest corner.

The wooden sections
Of the stairs seemed eerie and the
String-box seemed full of writhing snakes.

The lamp light
Flickered and danced on the newspapers
And on the tip of the bulb pushing its way out of the rich
earth.

Bother!
I cracked my head on the doorway
And painfully retired.

JANET CUTHBERT

The Princess

A hustle, a bustle, a flurry, a scurry,
Our princess is dying, oh, how we must hurry
And fetch the three doctors from over the way
Oh, hurry, the princess might die today!

The first doctor, said
    'Aha, ahum,
What she needs is a big currant bun'.
The second doctor said
    'Aha, aha,
What she needs is a ride in a car'
But the third doctor said
    'Aha, aha,
What she needs is to marry me'.

A hustle, a bustle, a flurry, a scurry
Our princess is married, Oh, how we must hurry
And ring the three bells from over the way,
Oh, hurry, the princess got married today!

JACQUELINE HILLYER

The Haunted Mansion

Ever so eerie,
Can't be more dreary,
Ghosts they begin to howl;
    Spooks in white,
    In an eerie dim light,
    Dance, to the hoot of the owl.

Now they advance,
More join the dance,
Most eerie a sight, but fine;
    Now 'tis calmer;
    But wait! the armour,
    Is shuffling into a line.

74

'We are all dead!'
Howled a ghost with no head,
No arms, no legs, yet so tall;
  'All your wills
  A compartment fills,
  Behind that panel in the wall.'

Scared of the spooks;
They were surely not flukes?
I crept softly out through the door;
  Getting over my fright
  I thought of that sight,
  And wished I had watched for
  some more.

JENNIFER BEARD

If

If birds had fins and they could swim
Into the murky water dim
Do you suppose they'd rather fly
Into the beautiful blue sky?
Do you think they'd stay on land?
Fly in the air, swim by the sand?

If fish had legs and they could walk
If they had tongues and they could talk
Would they be creatures just like me?
Prefer dry land to the wet sea
Write better poems than any man
Has ever done or ever can?

MICHAEL THOMPSON

The Face of
Things

Winter

The wind came whistling,
The rain came swishing,
So I shut my window and,
Went fast asleep.

SUSAN PARKER

Nothingness

At first the world was nothingness.
Not a rustle not a bustle not a blade of grass.
Not a tree not a house Just nothingness.

DAVID BATES

79

The Sun

The sun is big,
The sun is round,
But we'll hardly see it,
I'll be bound.

JUNE CRABTREE

Night

The sun has gone,
The moon takes its place,
All to bed we go.
The cricket purrs,
Insects too, go home to bed like you.

The night is long, The night is still
Man women child and nature sleep
    so peacefully,
Not knowing what the moon has
    seen with its silver gleem.
He has seen the grass lying round
    about,
The houses dark and dreary,
The trees still,
The waters ripling,
But not a person to be seen.

DOREEN VALERIE ABRAM

The Sea, The River and The Lake

The sea, the river and the lake.
Sh, sh, says the sea,
All the ships sail on me,
Sh, sh, says the sea I could blow down a tree,
When I send a storm all the sailors flee.

Lap, lap, says the river,
All the boats sail on me,
I always have to quiver,
Because I am a river,
And I always shiver and shiver.

Ripple, ripple, says the lake,
On me sails the drake,
The drake and his wife,
On me live their life.

ROBERT IAN BAILEY

Waves

There are big waves,
There are small waves,
There are lots of other waves to.
The big waves call
Hoo hoo hoo.

There are big waves,
There are small waves
There are waves you can jump over,
Waves that twist,
And waves that turn over.

JILL DOREEN SMITH

Snow, Past and Present Tense

Slowly, majestically, the snow comes down,
Covering all the dirt, grime and grit of the streets.
Covering it with firm, crisp, untouched snow
That has fallen in the night.
This is the sight I see from my bedroom window.
I yawn and I go back to bed.
But what is this?
I see brown footprints in the snow.
Brown footprints! Is nothing sacred?

STEPHEN GILLER

Snow

Snow—the beginning of an ice-age.
—Come quickly, Ma, come quick and look!
The boy runs in, terrified, ashen face
Distorted by fear.
—Eh, the devil's bin chasin' him, Gran says.
—Ay, 'e was so near
'E touched me! 'E's got a white cloak;
Does the devil always wear a white cloak?

—I remember when we had snow
Every year; ugh! how cold those winters were!—
Laugh now, for you'll cry
When I'm gone, when you're married and older,
When your children die—
Yes, laugh now, you'll cry then, *I* know . . .

—I think, 'twas in nineteen forty-eight;
The war had ended and winter begun.
My husband was dead—
Killed in action; and I, just thirty-one,
Was given to read
A certificate, telling his fate.

And honouring him. Small thanks, indeed,
For such a man—my husband, whom I love.
As for my children—
That winter and shortage of food was enough—
'Come here quickly, Gran,
Come quick and look, it's snowing!—Is it, indeed?'

ROSEMARY O'CONNOR

The Winds up to Mystery

Woo said the wind on a rainy afternoon,
'I've got a job to do tonight',
I will saw off someone's chimney,
I will break down someone's door,
That's the job I've got to do tonight.

Off went the wind at five o'clock at night,
Smashing fun I've got tonight he whispered in delight,
Here we are at last he said,
Now where did I put my saw,
The Wind sawed off a chimney pot,
And broke down someone's door.

LORRAINE BUFFERY

The Wind

The wind,
It is a ghostly hand
Pushing to and fro,
The leaves and stray paper
That lay scattered in his path.

The trees
Bow down to the strength
Of the whistling wind,
As though paying homage
To some unknown king.

N. CAREY

Leaves

Leaves are brown
Leaves are red.
  They all fling down
When the tree shakes its head.

DIANA FERGUSON

One Narcissus Plucked

Life has been stopped
In one big pull—
For a narcissus
Under a wall.

Poor little thing lost its life,
Lost its place
In the garden—
Its beauty will soon go.

Once it was a growing plant,
Healthy, wild and free
To blow in April wind.
Soon it will be a dead little thing.

NICHOLAS BANKES

The Canal at Coseley

Curling along like a slippery snake,
Runs the canal with its burly bridges,
And lumbering locks grey and creaking,
A home of jumping frogs, nervous newts,
Old iron bedsteads and rusty tin cans,
A watery grave for some unwanted dogs,
The abode of stately swans,
And splashing cygnets,
And rainbow coloured dragonflies,
Who dive and wheel
Over tall, slender bullrushes,
It is a watery road,
Used by chugging boats,
Carrying loads of coal,
Drums of tar and leaden pipes,
To the Midlands,
From the North,
Steered by unsmiling, lonely men,
Who guide them,

Staring in gloomy silence at us,
As they pass,
It seems as though it will pass away.
For the reeds grow tall,
It needs repairs,
And it soon dies,
But no one cares.

CAROL ELAINE HAWKINS

Wind, Waves and Sails

Crack of jibing canvas, dazzle-white in the sun,
The harsh cry of a marsh bird,
The flap of pennant in the breeze, or the slop of a halyard
On the mast.
The delicate staccato of wavelets on the waterline.

The shine on steel and sun-shocked
Varnished planking, slippery with moisture.
The scents of summer drifting from the shore.

We move sometimes wafted
By the soft finger-breezes,
Prodding the sail,
Delicate as death
While the world glides softly, swanlike, by.

And sometimes, the gunwale creams the water,
As,
Shell shock, cannon blast,
A squall billows out the shoulder of mutton,
And heels her with a giant sneeze.

86

Faintly,
From the land, the sound of crickets scraping
Their thin tin whistle piping
In the long straw grasses.

In the reeds
A fish jumps
Snapping greedily at some tasty, winged morsel.
The rudder creaks oil-lessly on its pintles,
The spars groan,
And all is liquid peace.

M. LA RUE

The Landscape

The huddles of grey stone cottages,
The piles of peat leaning against their walls,
The mournful lowing of the cattle in the farm-yard
And the blue smoke twisting into cold grey sky.

Against the narrow roadside stand the mud-filled dykes
While beyond is the great black bog
Stretching monotonously over the horizon,
Dotted with the dark skeletons of trees.

Then far away beyond all this
Stands the high sea-wall,
The foam-flecked waves lashing against it
And the sea-gulls hovering overhead.

JANE HORLOCK

In Campbell Street

In Mayfield Way the pavement's clean,
The people sober, calm, serene,
The children neither heard nor seen.
   It's not like that in Campbell Street!

The washing's rarely out all day,
And when it is, it's white, not grey;
The fog just seems to stay away.
   It's not like that in Campbell Street!

The diesel engines do not smoke,
Our people never cough and choke.
The air is clean—we all use coke.
   It's not like that in Campbell Street!

The dogs in our street never fight,
Our cats will neither scratch nor bite.
It's quiet enough to sleep at night.
   It's not like that in Campbell Street!

We never swing on garden gates,
We never fail to pay our rates,
We're never, ever, late from 'dates'.
   It's not like that in Campbell Street!

Our gardens, too, are all just so,
We never need to weed and hoe;
The hedges trim themselves. Oh no,
   It's not like that in Campbell Street!

In Campbell Street the organs play,
The people there are glad and gay,
And chaos reigns both night and day!
   I wish I lived in Campbell Street!

ROSEMARY WINN

Please Keep Off The Grass

A democratic state, they said,
A democratic land.
They printed little gold-edged notes
And hired a silver band.
You may say what you like, they said,
If you do as you're told,
So please keep off the grass, my friend,
In case the grass is sold.

PETER TINSLEY

The Ego Alone
and Lost

EGO LOST

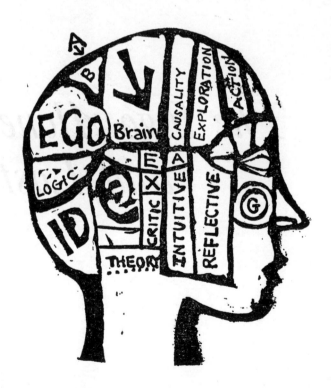

Quis ?

Who
are you
who sit singing
soft on the marble
threshold of the house of I,
the ego, alone and lost, but one
wailing red, outside the blind,
crystal gateways of
my mind alone.
Who are
You?

93

'No-one',
came back
the echoing reply
which lapped the brazen
pillars of the house of I,
the ego, alone and lost but one
who waited, trembling, inside,
at the golden wealth
of sound which spilled
liquidly over me.
'No-one'.

ANN DAVIES

The Painter

Not a bee buzzed,
Not a leaf stirred,
No bird flew upward towards the skies.
Crags of hard rock stood out against the glaring blue;
Nothing moved.

Alone in the heather sat the artist
With palette and brushes,
Trying to capture the solitude of the scene before him
That solitude that, like a cloak, threatened to envelop him.
As he worked, trees, bushes and heather took shape on his
    canvas;
All but solitude,
So apparent
So unattainable.

Soon the pale pink of departing day spread across the blue
  sky,
The pink turned to crimson and orange;
Then came the peace of twilight.

The lone painter, the only movement on the quiet scene,
  walked
Slowly homeward,
Back to the noise of the city.
And solitude was left
Upon the heath.

JENNIFER INGLIS

The Gallery

The gallery with its padded chairs
Stark and bare,
The faces in the pictures
Incapable of human thought
Stared at me.
They looked hard at me
As if to penetrate my innermost feelings
And make me one of them.
It unnerved me;
I wanted to escape
But I was paralysed
Until a small boy pointed at one of the pictures
And laughed.

JACQUELINE TRIEVNOR

One Day I Thought

One day I thought I would be a clown,
With a funny face and funny, funny clothes,
The next I thought I would be a writer
And write a book called WHO DONE IT!
Then I thought I would be a teacher
And teach English.
The next it was a model,
The next it was a star.
But when it came to choose a job,
I ended up in a biscuit factory.

NORMA SULLIVAN

Mother

My father wounded me last night
Bluntly, maliciously.
I turned my face concealing tears
That flooded to my head.

And there I stood and never spoke
A solitary word.
My soul so drenched with burning tears
How could I?

How could I turn my face to his
And show my swollen 'lids;
Expose my wretched, anguished soul
To watching, waiting eyes.

So while he watched me standing there
While he waited anxiously,
My painful tears began to ebb
Gave way to flowing reason.

Why had his malice cut my soul
To cause such sudden pain
That I broke down with inward sobs
And dared not turn his way?

For were his words completely true
Unprejudiced, unbent
Or had he twisted them in spite
Maliciously for me.

My mind recaptured infant-days
When I was by my mother
Ah yes, ah yes something was missing
In our togetherness.

A certain warmth and motherness
Was missing in her breast
Yet love was there, carressing me—
And sometimes comforting.

Now I was ready to turn my face
A smile upon my lips—
But as I turned the smile fell off:
No father saw I there.

JAMES MICHAEL POWER

Insensitive

He says, I am insensitive—
That I cannot feel the lithe wind
Catching my lips and
Breathing on them a fine white film—

That I cannot catch the finned
Fishes fretful plea of dreariness
Drifting round in the same
Round, insensitive, rudely staring bowl.
He says I am insensitive—
Not born to feel
The pulse and moving heart
Of others by me—
That I cannot open my charitable consciousness
So to be understanding and loving
Towards others.
He says I may never know
The ring of a truthful word
Or the depth of a tear's great span—
Or anything.
For you see, I have four walls
Which are built strongly—
Fat and stocky as the bulge of rosy cheeks
That bathe in the gushing sun
And whose skin is thrashed
In tune with the sugar cane melody
That coats the rustic plains
This I may never know—
For you see I am young,
(So he says)
And narrowly shaded
As a corner building in a crowded
Street—but wait!
I am not yet proven,
And your eyes are not piercing
Enough—your legs not supple enough
To climb my walls. You are blind
To me and all my standing.

SUSAN VAN COLLE

The Life and Soul of the Party

I should hate to be the life and soul of the party,
A rumbustrous blabbering fool,
Amusing others with his slick buffoonery,
Witty jokes, sly compliments and base flattery.
I should hate to lower myself to such inferior planes,
To live for the sodden gushes of gurgling giggles
And smutty smirks of others.

This is my pet hate, this, unakin to me—
Who keeps an unsuccessful party flowing firmly
Swiftly, to a grateful end;
Who keeps some distraught incompetent
Hostess happy,
Covered with smiles
And beaming rosily at her babbling guests.
Masculine he is, often small and oily,
Living all alone in a dirty Chelsea flat.
Lone and unattended, ekeing out his days
Until his time is done, and he will die,
Unnoticed and unmissed,
Merely a name
Crossed off his host's guest list.

Poor man, all that his memory lives for
Are long past revels in liquate, scented air,
Of low-cut draperies
Enclosing shapely females
Entrenched secretly and tightly in costly scented corsetry.

For memory he lives,
In memory he will die.
And when his time is done,

Will the world revive his stories,
Retell his dirty memories
Of chorus-girls long dead,
And actors in their under-pants?

His reign is in the evening,
When Summer breathes her scented air on early closing
    flowers.
His kingdom is the smoke-filled room,
His sceptre is a cigarette,
His crown a wreath of laughter.

Alone he lies in smelly earthy squalor,
His brain by death is numbed,
At him they laughed in life,
Will any grieve in death?

SUSAN STANTON

Blindness

We, who carelessly treasured our sight in childhood,
Cannot know the pain of waking
On life's first morning,
And opening expectant eyes on darkness;
Finding not light but loneliness.

You, who have never known
The meaning of purple; the shape of a mountain;
Whose hands, as sensitive as nerves, can never feel
The swoop of a bird's flight,
Or the mucous plait
Of your dying cigarette:
Which is the sweeter to you: life or death?

VIRGINIA GARDNER

Take Me Home

Mommy Daddy take me home
From this convalescent home
I've been here a year or two
Now I want to be with you.
Here comes Docter Bannister
Sliding down the bannister
Here comes nurse with a
red hot poultice,
Slaps it on and takes no
notice.
Oh! said the children is it hot?
Oh! said the nurse I'm sure
it's not.

STEPHEN WILSON

Annex 3

Here I lie in annex 3.
Getting better with my crooket toes
Never mind my muttered cure
We have got a smashing lot of nurses

English, Irish, Welsh and Scotch
Yes we have got the lot,
Late at night they come to see
If we're fast asleep

Every morning just at five
They come to see if we're alive
Then we all awake to see
That early morning cup of tea

LESLIE DAVIES

The Time When I Was Very Sad

The time when I was very sad
Was when we lost my Father's dad.
They took him to hospital where they looked after him,
But they said he made an awful din.

They put him in the operating room
Until he was ready to go in his tomb.
His coffin was very nice,
And he was in his grave in a trice.

PATRICIA

My Baby

My Mum's gone into hospital today
Hip-hip-horray, Hip-hip-horray
I love my Mum going into hospital today

She's having a baby
Today, today, today,
Horray

GILLIAN MARTIN

The Skyscraper

Someone said, 'I shall build a skyscraper';
The world laughed.
Ideas were put together for this miraculous ambition;
Models were made, plans were sketched
And a site was spotted.
Then men were employed and foundations laid.

Each brick was a step to fulfilment;
Walls, doorways, stairs and window-frames developed.
The ground floor was completed,
And so grew the second, third and fourth floors.
When the building consisted of fifteen storeys
The world began to take notice.
Eyes then looked up to the thirtieth floor with amazement.

When the building grew to sixty floors
The world applauded,
And used the skyscraper for offices.

ROSALYN LEVY

A Paris Drain

While walking past the river Seine
   My foot slipped and got stuck in a drain.
I was there from morn till night
   Till a gendarme came in sight.
He came with crow-bar, saw and file
   And tried to free me for a while.
Though his effort was in vain
   He came back and tried again.

MICHAEL KNIGHT

Don't Try To Be Funny

I tried to make him laugh
By standing on my head

I tried to make him laugh
By rushing what I said

I tried to make him laugh
By sawing up the bed

I tried to make him laugh
By grunting while I read

I tried to make him laugh
By saying I was dead

I tried to make him laugh
By pulling down the shed

I tried to make him laugh—
But I laughed at him instead.

A. PATTERSON

The Gods Don't Know

People, people, sitting, standing,
People gathered in a crowded room.
Ideas infinite and complex flow,
Spoken, hinted and deduced,
Theories passing wave-like across a mental sea,
Accepted or rejected as the case may be,
Give rise to inner striving on the bounds of pain.

Knowledge is the tinkle of glasses being filled,
Ignorance the misty smoke which hangs about the room.
Time becomes forgotten, lost in a haste to know,
And so forgotten passes from existence in a word.
Now people twine and intertwine ideas,
Caught in each other's web of words,
And lost in a tapestry of thought
They've weaved through hours of senseless joy.

Each fresh tangle of the threads of mind
Twists a little more the strained
And fragile fabric of their lives.
Where leads this endless path of social man,
The irrational force which drives these mortals on?
Ask not the gods, oh listeners,
For the gods don't know.

PETER TINSLEY

Alterations

A Fire

A cigarette end.
Dry leaves.
A slight breeze.
Flickering flames.
A cloud of smoke.
Spreading flames.
A dry bush.
Leaping flames.
A flying spark.
Dry grass.
A growing wind.
Roaring flames.
A frightened rabbit.
Burning trees.
A roasted rabbit.
Grasping flames.
Black clouds of smoke.
Flaming branches.
A wide, deep, river.
Drying flames.
A blackened forest.
Sizzling twigs.
A charred tree stump.
Flickering flames.

BRUCE MIDDLETON

The Fire

'Look out!' yelled the firemen
'It's a-coming down.'
'Look out!' gasped the crowd that was ranged around.
The blazing inferno, that once was a house,
Now eaten with fire, like a cat eats a mouse,
The heat was intense, and the air was thick,
The inmates were rescued, but the house was a stick.

Poor old thing, she once was so proud,
Of beautiful structure, and nose in the cloud,
And from the grounds, to the turrets, where the doves
    were a-coo-in',
A misguided flame had brought it to ruin.

MICHAEL GOULDSBOROUGH

Mars The God of War

B-B-B-O-O-O-M-M-M
MARS . . . the god of war was angry.
Lightning rent the air with flashes;
Rain, snow, hailstones pelted down with gathering force.
'STOP! STOP!' cried Jupiter . . . No heed was paid.
Animals, trees, crops, women, men, their kin, bent under the
    terrible fury.
The waters rose until . . . until a swirling torrent of water
    broke through the dykes.
A deluge of water rushed through the country,
The hated hand of Mars guiding the torrent
Swallowing all in its path . . . drowning, demolishing.

Panic-stricken people ran, the church bells rang their
  warning . . . the first in sixty years . . .
Until . . . until at last the torrent stopped . . . in a field of
  red tulips,
The sun shone . . . Mars fled beaten.

JIMMY HAMILTON

The Rain Dance

The fire flickered with a flare,
The ghostly figure leapt in the air.
Huge shadows fell across the ground
When the figure landed without any sound.
A piercing scream, a bongo beat,
A tossing head, two stamping feet,
Legs bent at knees, feet wide apart,
A twisting body, a thudding heart.
The drums beat out, loud and clear.
D-rr-um-dum-dum, the time draws near.
The twirling body leaps again
Trying hard to make it rain.

MARINA BRUNSKILL

A Prison

A prison is like a great gaunt castle,
With great big walls and doors
Studded with spikes,
As if to keep a herd of elephants inside,
But only men are there.

Inside are great long passages,
With cells on either side.
Long, dark and spooky,
With warders pacing them up and down,
To see that no man escapes.

But even with great big walls and doors,
And all the precautions of guards and warders
Men still escape,
And slip over the great big wall like
December spooks,
But they are brought back.

K. ASH

Hiroshima

The bomb burst like a flower,
And grew upwards under the sun.
And men stood afar off, and wondered,
What was the meaning of this?
Then the flower died, and they partly forgot,
What had happened that summer day.

But in later years terror reigned in the land,
For the deadly blight of the flower had fallen on men
And as they died, they cried to the stars to avenge,
This inhumanity of man to man.

And future generations inherited,
A sorrow, and a remembrance of it,
And a lesson drawn from their ancestors' futility

ANGELA M. CLIFTON

This Modern Age

This modern age, it seems to me,
Is full of opportunity.
'Times have changed,' our parents say;
I wonder if they'll stay this way.

Gone by is the age of stone,
Of lavender and lace;
I think I rather like this
Modern age of space.

Who knows what fun we'll have,
For very, very soon
With luck we'll orbit round the earth
Or travel to the moon.

Just think, how great it is
To fly among the stars,
And even pay a visit to
Mercury or Mars.

Yes, I think this modern age
Has such a lot to give
They can keep their carriages,
I just want to live!

BRYAN REED

Washing-Up

I had just heard those dreaded words, which all at some time
   hear,
And slowly to the sink I went and saw what I did fear,
A pile of dirty, greasy crocks all waiting for the mop;
I groaned at the ghastly sight and, looking to the top,
Said, 'English, History, Maths and French all to be done
   tonight
And so you see, my Mother dear, I'm in a sorry plight
And I'm afraid that I can't do the washing up tonight.'

MARGARET BRAND

Our House

In our house there are many rooms,
If you were to sweep it
You'd need many brooms.
A duster for this, and a duster for that,
And a nice new Hoover
To clean our new mat.

JUDITH D. GRATTON

Our Dustbin

Nobody makes poems about dustbins
So I will.
For a dustbin is of interest too.
Cats like poking around smelling bones.

When the dustman comes to collect
The rubbish
You can hear the tin go along, clang! clang!
When he empties it the dust rises
And goes whirling to the sky.
Bits of china shine in the sun
And bright things I wish I could look at.

DOUGLAS CUFF

The Dictator

Enriquez is dead, Gonzalez lives,
The rebels with blessings are showered.
'Gonzalez is brave, Gonzalez is strong,
Enriquez was a coward.'

Gonzalez is now the president,
'Long may he live,' the people cry,
'Gonzalez is brave, Gonzalez is strong,
Enriquez deserved to die'.

Gonzalez has grown a mighty man,
'His rule is harsh,' the people sigh,
'Gonzalez is cruel, Gonzalez is strong,
Gonzalez now deserves to die.'

Gonzalez is a frightened man,
'Long live Ruiz', the people cry,
'Ruiz is brave, Ruiz is strong,
'Gonzalez, he must die.'

Gonzalez is dead, Ruiz now rules,
'Long may he live,' the people cry.
Although dictators are brave and strong,
Freedom must never die!

H. BAILEY

A Child is Born

A baby is born rejoice
How quiet not a noise.
Born in a manger
To save us from danger.
He was to teach
Love and preach.
Angels sang
As the sheep bells rang.
Shepherds were curious
Herod was furious.
So now we keep Christmas day
Lovely joyous and gay.

MARY ANN HAMBURGER

Pistons

Trains

Trains are snorting monsters,
Running on snaky railway lines.

An express train at night is like a jewelled snake,
Writhing round the curves in the track.

A goods train is like a line of dirty men,
Plodding home after a hard day's work.

But I like trains.

K. ASH

Blackpool Tower Lift

Up down, up down,
Its slow motion route
Continues.
As of a tram on a lonesome road,
Engulfing people, and pinning them
Behind its slide-long teeth
Of criss-cross iron grip.
Button A—and
With a gush of heaven-borne wind
It soars like a bird
Away from earth.

Wait for us, wait,
The buildings seem to cry,
   As higher,
Higher up it crawls
Leaving the spotted dots of shoppers,
   And matchbox cars,
And squares of bricks.
   Button B—and
Crash, it bangs to a halt!
   The sea beneath
   One mass of blue.

MARJORIE THWAITE

The Train

The train came down the track
With a heavy load on its back.
   It said, 'Puff, puff!
   I've had enough!'
The train came down the track.

JANE MARCINOWSKA

An Engine

An engine came puffing along the track,
Puff, puff, puff, with the fireman inside
   All rosy and fat.
The hills and the trees all cheer and laugh,
When the train comes shunting along the track.

PATRICIA BLACKBURN

Over the Ocean

Roly poly over the waves:
Dames and ladies and little knaves,
Cats and dogs and clodhoppy horses,
Go over the ocean wide.

Roly poly over the waves:
'Kiticat' and 'All-in-One' and Farmer Brown's best hay,
Umbrellas and purses and long pointed spears,
Go over the ocean wide.

Roly poly over the waves:
In a big liner they go—
Little things we send for others' needs—
Over the ocean wide.

JILL PEARSON

A Bundle of Old Lead-coated Electric Cable

Shaped like snakes coiled round and round,
So old, so heavy, so tangled too,
Its paint is flaked, and the wires end,
Beyond a junction box, like barrels from a gun.

The lead is running round itself,
To hide, to wait for a kill.
Its been on the wall for many a year—
Now, free from the cage, it seeks revenge.

PETER WATERFIELD

Pondering on a Puddle in the Playground

In a corner of our playground
Is a puddle long and wide.
In it is a piece of stick—
A wrecked old ship,
Blown to pieces by a shell—
With not a sole survivor.
Bits of leaves are shattered wreckage,
And under the water lie the sailors, dead.

ROBERT REDFORD

A Sputnik

A sputnik one night
Went up for a flight.
It started to rain
So it came down again.

JUNE SMITH

The M.1

Slowly edging up the slope
On the M.1—full of hope.
A burst of speed, the throttle down,
We fly past village, field and town.

122

A heavy lorry with a load
We pass along the grand new road.
There are no signs to cause a fuss
Nor folk alighting from a bus.

No bikes or children are seen there,
We speed along without a care.
Swishing, swooshing passed each other,
Under bridge and o'er another.

Faster, faster, o'er and under,
On and on with miles to go.
All the cars—they sound like thunder—
Never think of going slow.

Now we're near our journey's end;
We leave the M.1 round the bend,
In to the left lane, drive more slow,
And off the highway we will go.

JANE ASHFORD